the music
glee™
playalong
for flute

Wise Publications
part of The Music Sales Group
London / New York / Paris / Sydney / Copenhagen / Berlin / Madrid / Hong Kong / Tokyo

C000228010

Published by
Wise Publications
14-15 Berners Street, London W1T 3LJ, UK.

Exclusive distributors:
Music Sales Limited
Distribution Centre,
Newmarket Road, Bury St Edmunds, Suffolk, IP33 3YB, UK.
Music Sales Pty Limited
20 Resolution Drive, Caringbah, NSW 2229, Australia.

Order No. AM1001176
ISBN 978-1-84938-626-5

Engraving and arranging supplied by Camden Music.
Backing tracks by Paul Honey.
Flute played by Howard McGill.
Edited by Lizzie Moore.

Printed in the EU.

Your Guarantee of Quality

As publishers, we strive to produce every book to the highest
commercial standards. The music has been freshly engraved and
the book has been carefully designed to minimise awkward page
turns and to make playing from it a real pleasure.

Particular care has been given to specifying acid-free, neutral-sized
paper made from pulps which have not been elemental chlorine bleached.

This pulp is from farmed sustainable forests and was
produced with special regard for the environment.

Throughout, the printing and binding have been planned to ensure a sturdy,
attractive publication which should give years of enjoyment.

If your copy fails to meet our high standards, please inform us
and we will gladly replace it.

www.musicsales.com

Flute Fingering Chart

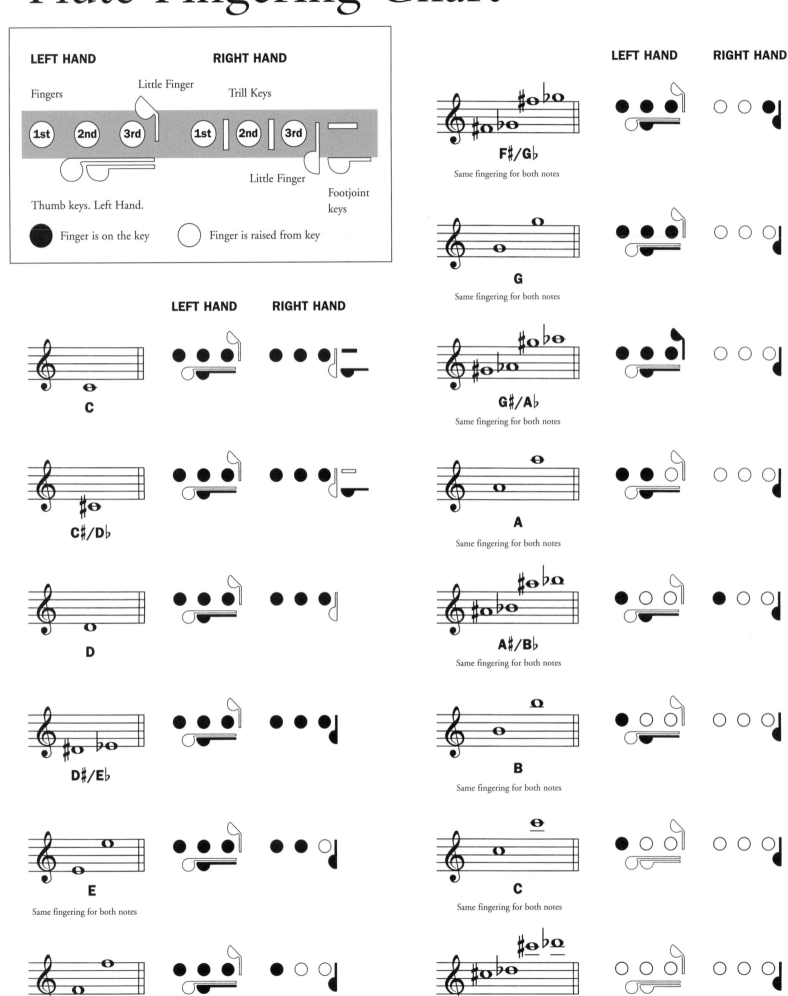

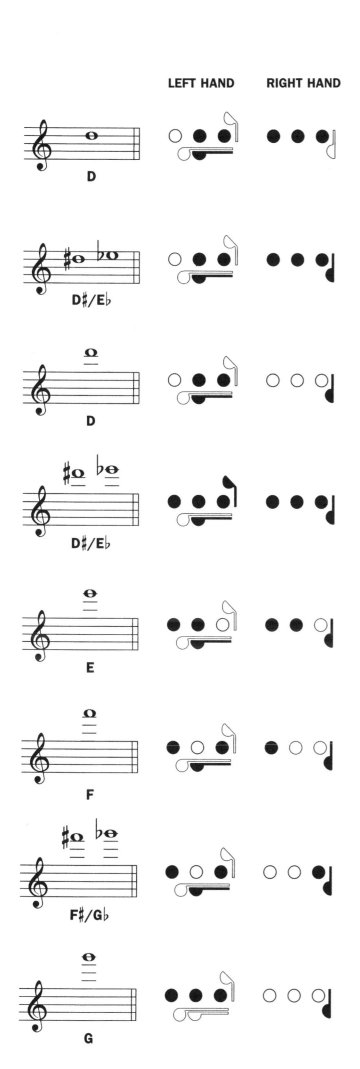
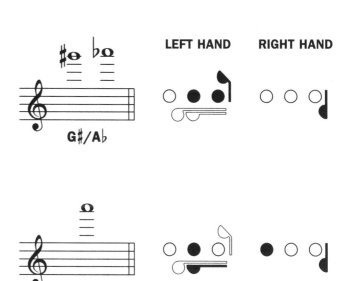
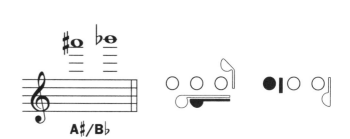
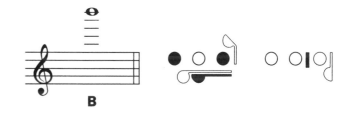
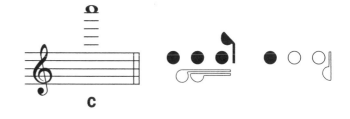

Alone

Words & Music by Billy Steinberg & Tom Kelly

Defying Gravity

Words & Music by Stephen Schwartz

9

Don't Stop Believin'

Words & Music by Steve Perry, Neal Schon & Jonathan Cain

I'll Stand By You

Words & Music by Chrissie Hynde, Tom Kelly & Billy Steinberg

Can't Fight This Feeling

Words & Music by Kevin Cronin

D.S. al Coda

Coda

molto rit.

Like A Prayer

Words & Music by Madonna & Pat Leonard

Rhythmically, with a bounce

Softly and smoothly

mf

mp

mf legato

f

mf energico

No Air

Words & Music by Harvey Mason, Damon Thomas, James Fauntleroy, Erik Griggs & Steven Russell

Physical

Words & Music by Steve Kipner & Terry Shaddick

Rhythmically, with energy ♩ = 124

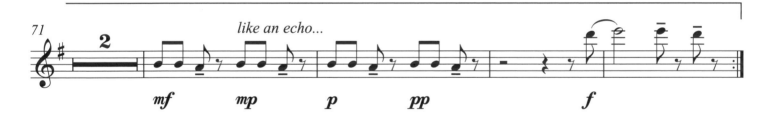

Poker Face

Words & Music by Stefani Germanotta & Nadir Khayat

Mechanically ♩ = 119

True Colours

Words & Music by Billy Steinberg & Tom Kelly

(guitar solo)

molto rit.

123456789

ALSO AVAILABLE

For more information on these and the thousands of
other titles available from Wise Publications and Chester Music, please contact:

Music Sales Limited
Newmarket Road, Bury St Edmunds, Suffolk, IP33 3YB.
www.musicsales.com

TRACK LISTING:

CD 1 - DEMONSTRATION TRACKS

1. Tuning note
2. Alone
(Steinberg/Kelly)
Sony/ATV Music Publishing (UK) Limited
3. Defying Gravity
(from the Broadway Musical Wicked)
(Schwartz)
Greydog Music
4. Don't Stop Believin'
(Perry/Schon/Cain)
Alfred Music Publishing Company Incorporated/
Sony/ATV Music Publishing (UK) Limited
5. I'll Stand By You
(Hynde/Kelly/Steinberg)
EMI Music Publishing Limited/Kobalt Music Publishing Limited
6. Can't Fight This Feeling
(Cronin)
Hornall Brothers Music Limited
7. Like A Prayer
(Madonna/Leonard)
Warner/Chappell Music Publishing Limited/EMI Music Publishing Limited/
Sony/ATV Music Publishing (UK) Limited
8. No Air
(Mason/Thomas/Fauntleroy/Griggs/Russell)
Universal Music Publishing Limited/
EMI Music Publishing Limited/Universal Music Publishing MGB
9. Physical
(Kipner/Shaddick)
EMI April Music Incorporated
10. Poker Face
(Germanotta/Khayat)
Sony/ATV Music Publishing
11. True Colours
(Steinberg/Kelly)
Sony/ATV Music Publishing (UK) Limited

CD 2 - BACKING TRACKS ONLY

1. Tuning note
2. Alone
3. Defying Gravity
4. Don't Stop Believin'
5. I'll Stand By You
6. Can't Fight This Feeling
7. Like A Prayer
8. No Air
9. Physical
10. Poker Face
11. True Colours